GIGANTIC
COLORING AND ACTIVITY BOOK

DREAMWORKS

Trolls
TOUR

DREAMWORKS

DreamWorks Trolls World Tour
© 2020
DreamWorks Animation LLC.
All Rights Reserved.

bendon®

The BENDON name, logo and Tear and Share are trademarks of Bendon, Ashland, OH 44805.

LET'S DRAW!

Trace the gray lines to finish
the drawing of Hickory!

Count 'Em Up

How many treble clefs do you see?

Your Answer

TRANSFER

Using the paths, transfer the letters into the circles below to unscramble the word.

S R E E N W T

◯ ◯ ◯ ◯ ◯ ◯ ◯

SQUARES

Taking turns, connect a line from one heart to another. Whoever makes the line that completes the square puts his or her initial in the square. The person with the most squares at the end of the game wins!

TIC-TAC-TOE

Play a game of Tic-Tac-Toe with a friend!

Use the grid to draw
TROLLZART.

Which is Different?

Which picture of Guy Diamond is different from the others?

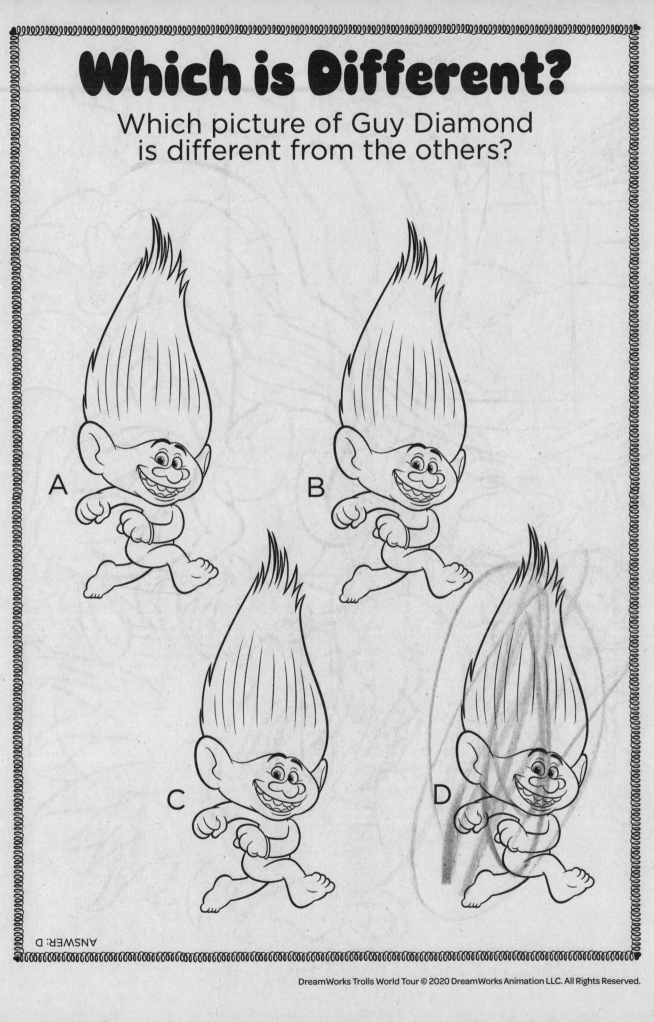

A

B

C

D

How many words can you make
from the letters in the phrase below?

Sing Your Heart Out

_____   _____

_____   _____

_____   _____

_____   _____

_____   _____

_____   _____

_____   _____

_____   _____

_____   _____

_____   _____

_____   _____

Follow the Path

Find your way through the puzzle by following the word **L-O-N-E-S-O-M-E-F-L-A-T-S** in order.

START

```
L O A C P O E S L X
A N D U G K B T S Y
G E H P N B J I W X
O S F S L O N E S O
M D C T U R K O F M
E F L A N V E L F E
H W H M D G I A J R
F Q L C F J V T B A
Z N T I Y X M S Q K
```

FINISH

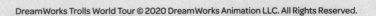

Interlock

Complete the puzzle by using
the words from the list.

VOLUME · BEAT
HARMONY · PEACE
SYMPHONY · DANCE

A=MAZE=ING JOURNEY

Help Poppy make her way to the strings!

FINISH

START

ANSWER:

TROLLZART

Find Fourteen

Look forward, backward, up, down, and diagonally to find the word below 14 times.

ROCK

```
K K C R K R O C K R
R R R O C R O C K C C
K K O R O C K R C R
C O R O C K R R K O
O K O O K R C K C O
R O C K C C R R O C
O O K C R K C O R R
C K C R O C K R C K
K R C O R R O K C O
```

Shadow Match

Which shadow matches Poppy?

A

B

C

Which Path?

Which path leads Hickory to Delta Dawn?

A

B

C

Your
Answer

ANSWER: A

DreamWorks Trolls World Tour © 2020 DreamWorks Animation LLC. All Rights Reserved.

Dot-to-Dot

Got dot-to-dot to finish
the picture of Poppy!

DRAW

The home of the Funk Trolls is Vibe City, which is inside a giant flying saucer!

Draw a picture of your own spaceship home!

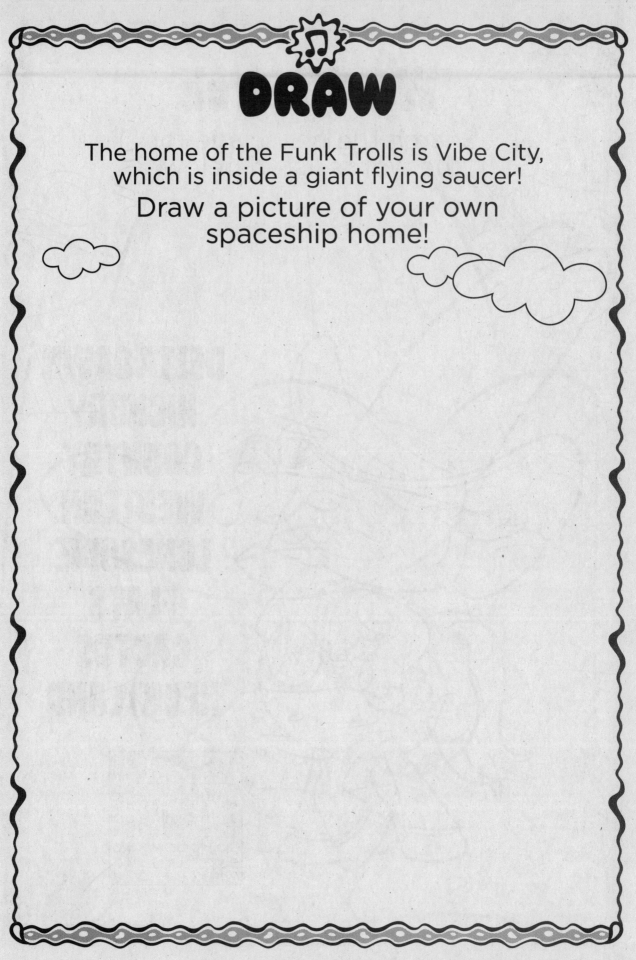

Word Search

Search the next page for
the words listed below.

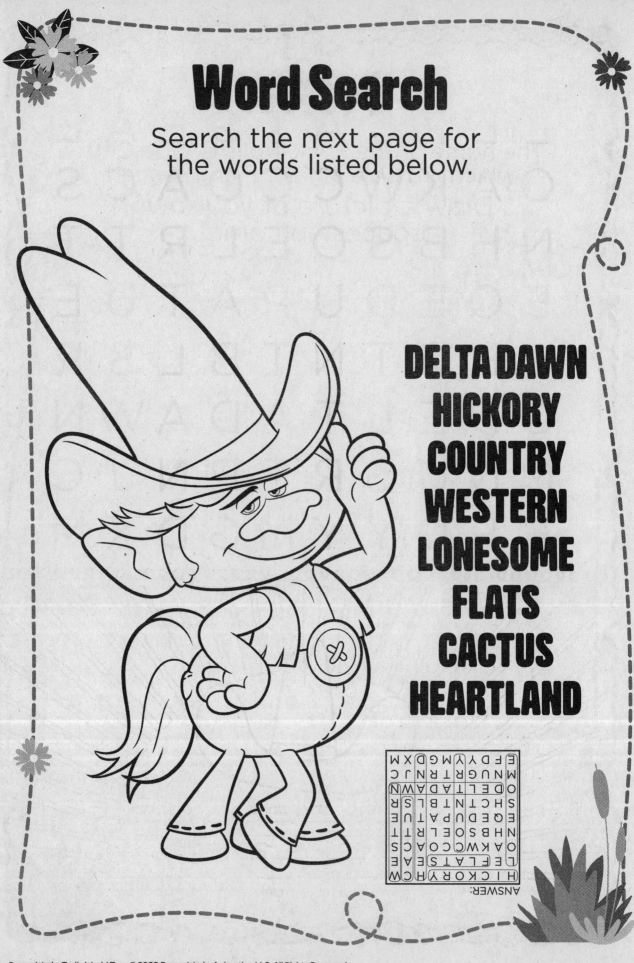

DELTA DAWN
HICKORY
COUNTRY
WESTERN
LONESOME
FLATS
CACTUS
HEARTLAND

ANSWER:

```
H I C K O R Y H C W
L E F L A T S E A E
O A K W C C O A C S
N H B S O E L R T T
E Q E D U P A T U E
S H C T N T B L S R
O D E L T A D A W N
M N U G R T R N J C
E F D Y Y M G D X M
```

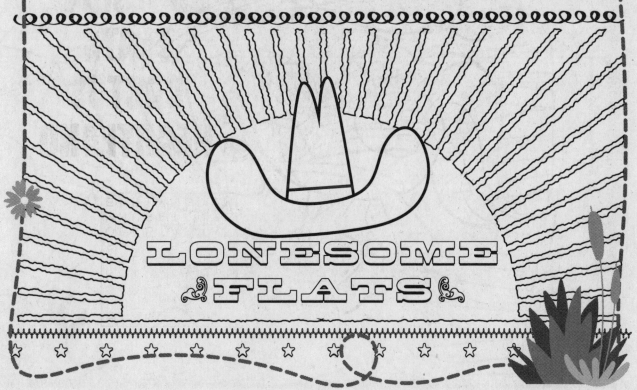

UNSCRAMBLE

Unscramble the words listed below.

_____
BVEI

_____
IYTC

_____
KUFN

_____
SICMU

_____
MAOCHANIR

_____
UFYKN

_____
EASTB

_____
FINGLY

_____
AUCRES

LET'S DRAW!

Trace the gray lines to finish
the drawing of King Quincy!

Secret Message

Use the key to decipher
the secret message.

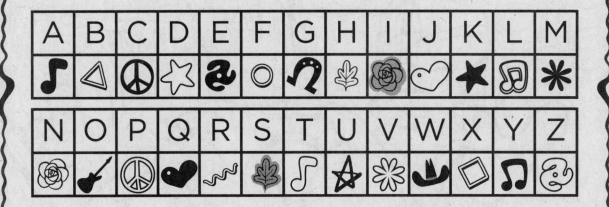

TRANSFER

Using the paths, transfer the letters into the circles below to unscramble the word.

E C E I R F

Count 'Em Up

How many roller skates do you see?

Your Answer

Use the grid to draw RIFF.

Troll Match

Which two pictures of Hickory are the same?

A

B

C

D

LET'S SAVE MUSIC

How many words can you make
from the letters in the phrase below?

Pump Up the Volume

_____   _____

_____   _____

_____   _____

_____   _____

_____   _____

_____

_____

_____

_____

_____

SQUARES

Taking turns, connect a line from one peace symbol to another. Whoever makes the line that completes the square puts his or her initial in the square. The person with the most squares at the end of the game wins!

Which is Different?

Which picture of Poppy is different from the others?

TIC-TAC-TOE

Play a game of Tic-Tac-Toe with a friend!

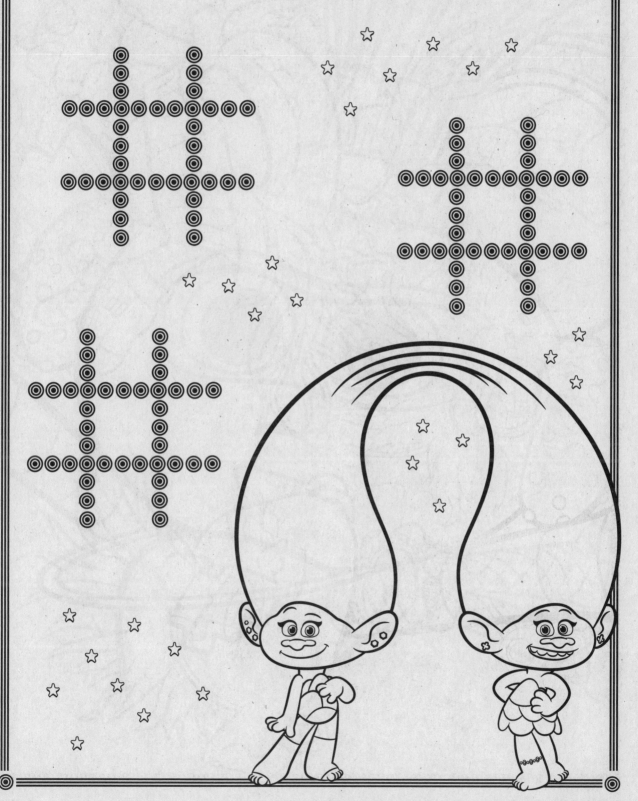

MISSING PIECE

Find the missing piece of the image and finish the drawing of Queen Poppy!

A-MAZE-ING JOURNEY

Help Prince D get to his brother Cooper!

START

FINISH

ANSWER:

Can you find 5
HORSESHOES
hidden below?

Find Fourteen

Look forward, backward, up, down, and diagonally to find the word below 14 times.

VIBE

```
E I B V B E E V V B
E I V E I I B I I I
B V I B E B I V B E
V I E B B B I I E E
E E E V I E V B V B
B E B I V I B E E I
I V E I I E B I B V
V I B E B E B I V B
V E I B E E V E B I
```

Shadow Match

Which shadow matches Poppy?

Which Path?

Which path leads the techno mermaid to King Trollex?

A

B

C

Your Answer

ANSWER: A

DRAW

Trollzart and the Classical Trolls
fly around their home, Symphonyville.
If you could fly like a Classical
Troll, where would you go?

Dot-to-Dot

Go dot-to-dot to finish the picture of Amp!

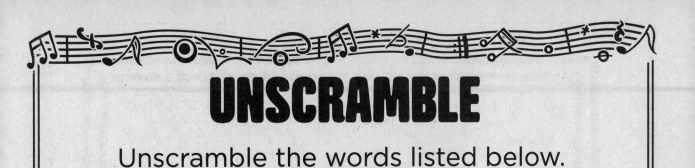

UNSCRAMBLE

Unscramble the words listed below.

URONDCCTO

SWIGN

ILLAASSCC   **SMICU**

TELUF

RESTRACHO

LET'S DRAW!

Trace the gray lines to finish
the drawing of Branch!

Interlock

Complete the puzzle by using the words from the list.

DELTA
DAWN
COUNTRY
WESTERN
LONESOME
FLATS

TRANSFER

Using the paths, transfer the letters into the circles below to unscramble the word.

Y H M H R T

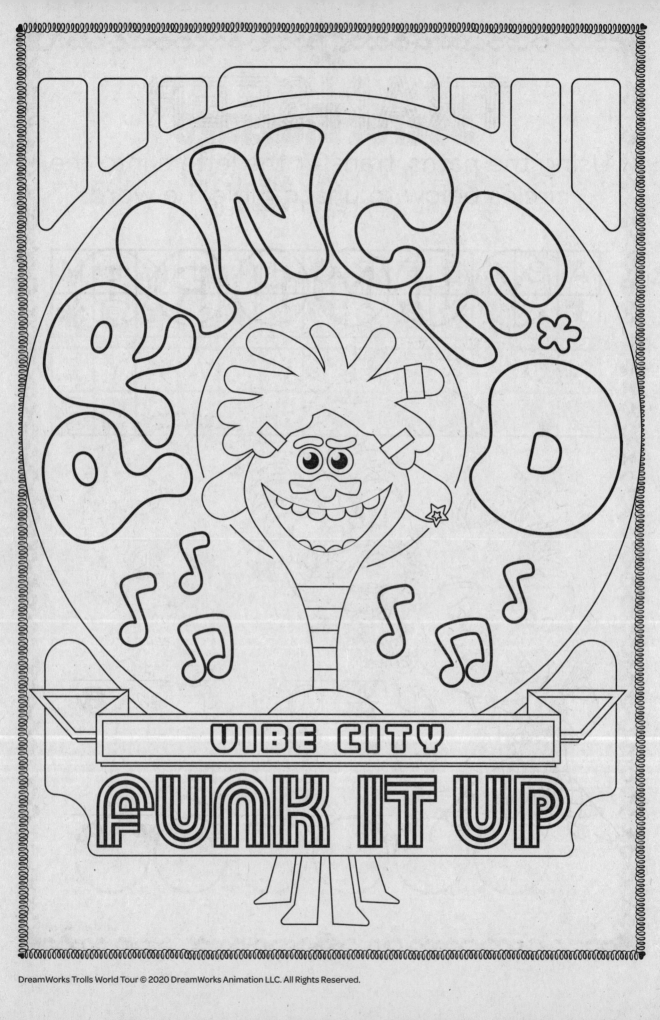

Secret Message

Use the key to decipher
the secret message.

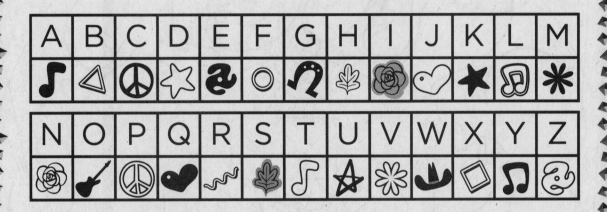

Use the grid to draw POPPY.

Count 'Em Up

How many hearts do you see?

Your
Answer

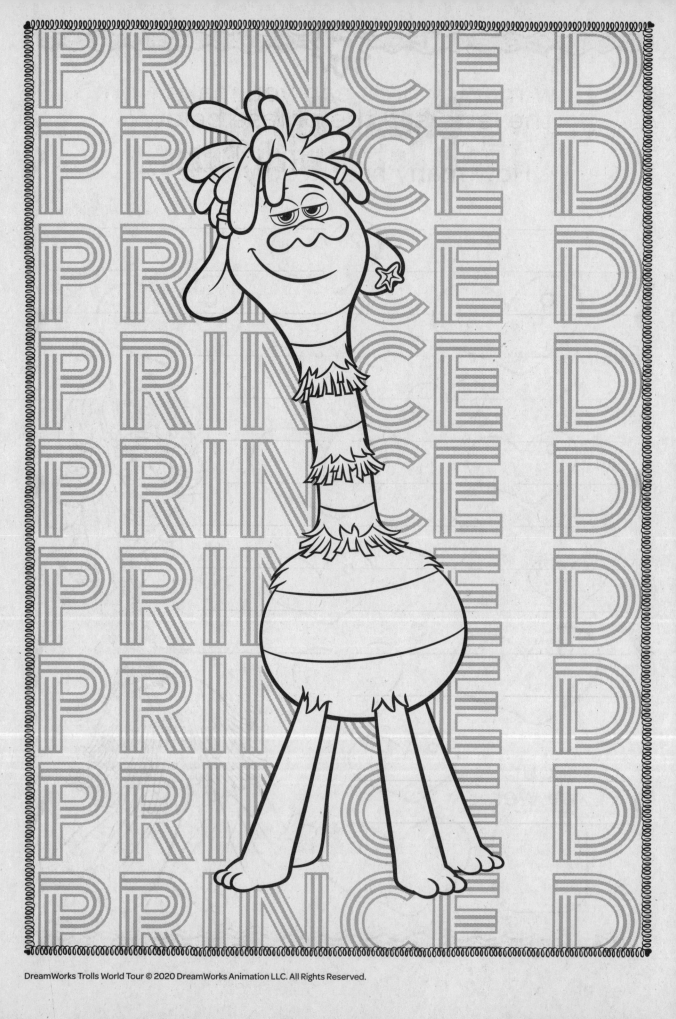

How many words can you make from the letters in the phrase below?

Life Is Better with Music

Follow the Path

Find your way through the puzzle by following the word **V-O-L-C-A-N-O-R-O-C-K-C-I-T-Y** in order.

START

(V) A O R O C U N H L
O B N D L K D J A Q
L C A F E C R Y P E
K T H Y T I X P G N
O B S V W K Q J S T
T I F O L C A N O R
A C G E S I W D B O
X O M Z C G I C K C
C A U F M H T (Y) R L

FINISH

Troll Match

Which two pictures of Poppy are the same?

A

B

C

D

MISSING PIECE

Find the missing piece of the image and finish the drawing of Prince D!

SQUARES

Taking turns, connect a line from one French horn to another. Whoever makes the line that completes the square puts his or her initial in the square. The person with the most squares at the end of the game wins!

Which is Different?

Which picture of Poppy is different from the others?

TIC-TAC-TOE

Play a game of Tic-Tac-Toe with a friend!

Interlock

Complete the puzzle by using
the words from the list.

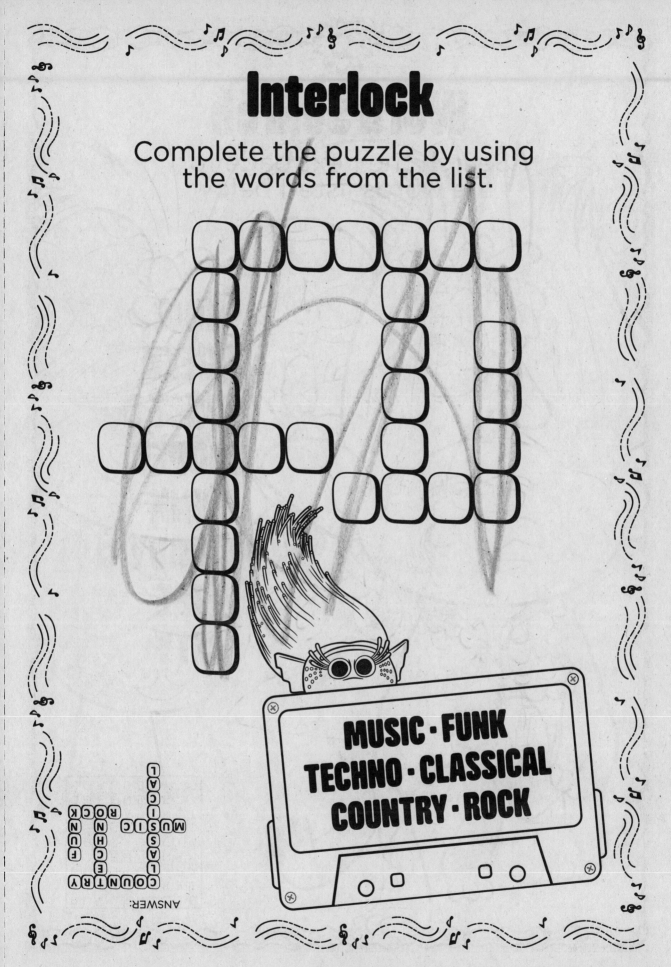

**MUSIC · FUNK
TECHNO · CLASSICAL
COUNTRY · ROCK**

ANSWER:

Word Search

Search the next page for
the words listed below.

KING

QUEEN

PRINCE D

COOPER

FUNK

GROOVY

VIBE

CITY

ANSWER:

```
S O P G D B K M D O
Q U E E N E P S E Y
I R S D W F T N C T
X E G R O O V Y I I
M P A E J B G I G C
Y O E F U N K N R H
E O B C D G V I H P
L C I K F L O K P A
R U V C R N I Q J E Z
```

Guy Diamond & Tiny Diamond

A-MAZE-ING JOURNEY

Help Queen Barb
get to Riff!

START

FINISH

ANSWER:

Find Fourteen

Look forward, backward, up, down, and diagonally to find the word below 14 times.

♫ MUSIC ♪

```
U C C I S U I U M I
M M S C M U C M U S
C U U I C I M U S U
I S M S U M U S I C
C I S U M U S I C M
S C U M U S I C U U
I U M U S I C S M C
S M U S I C U C S I
M U S I C C S I U S
```

DRAW

The Country Western Trolls live in Lonesome Flats, where all the buildings are shaped like cactuses!

Draw a picture of what your house would look like in Lonesome Flats.

Shadow Match

Which shadow matches Smidge?

A

B

C

UNSCRAMBLE

Unscramble the words listed below.

_____   _____
LEONMOES   LSATF

_____
ACTESCSU

_____   _____
OCYBOW   HTA

_____
ROOSESHESH

_____
BJOAN

LET'S DRAW!

Trace the gray lines to finish
the drawing of Riff!

Dot-to-Dot

Go dot-to-dot to finish the picture of Poppy!

TRANSFER

Using the paths, transfer the letters into the circles below to unscramble the word.

N Y U K F

○ ○ ○ ○ ○

Use the grid to draw the TECHNO MERMAID.

Which Path?

Which path leads
the Troll kids to
Biggie and Mr. Dinkles?

A B C

Your
Answer

ANSWER: B

How many words can you make from the letters in the phrase below?

Music Is the Journey

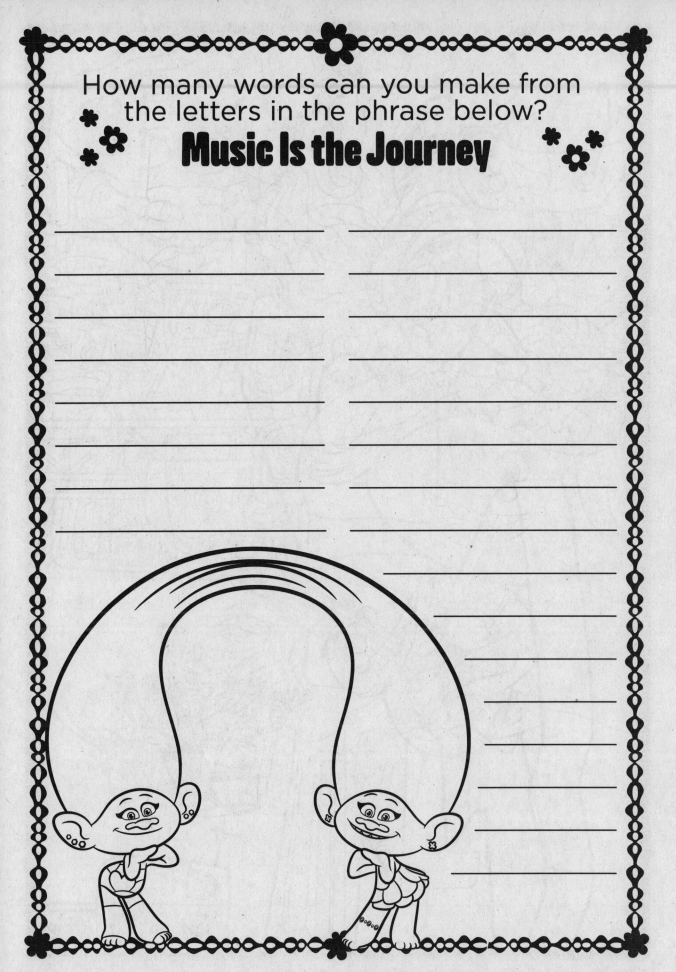

_____   _____

_____   _____

_____   _____

_____   _____

_____   _____

_____   _____

_____   _____

_____

_____

_____

_____

_____

Secret Message

Use the key to decipher
the secret message.

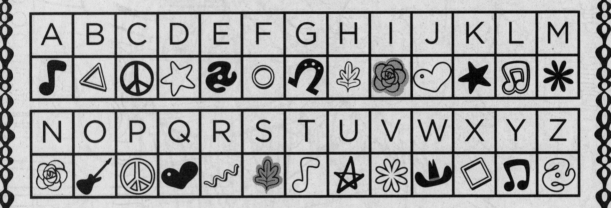

Count 'Em Up

How many sunglasses do you see?

Your Answer

MISSING PIECE

Find the missing piece of the image and finish the drawing of Queen Barb!

①

②

③

Follow the Path

Find your way through the puzzle by following the word **M-U-S-I-C-I-S-L-I-F-E** in order.

START

M D F S D Y N O J X
U I B M I E Z H A S
S H B F E M U S I C
I A E I R A E J L I
C I S L O F B D U S
L Q W T K T T G N L
X D U C L C S C A I
R G H N F O V M K F
X P J W I G P P M E

FINISH

Troll Match

Which two pictures of Poppy are the same?

Which is Different?

Which picture of Smidge is different from the others?

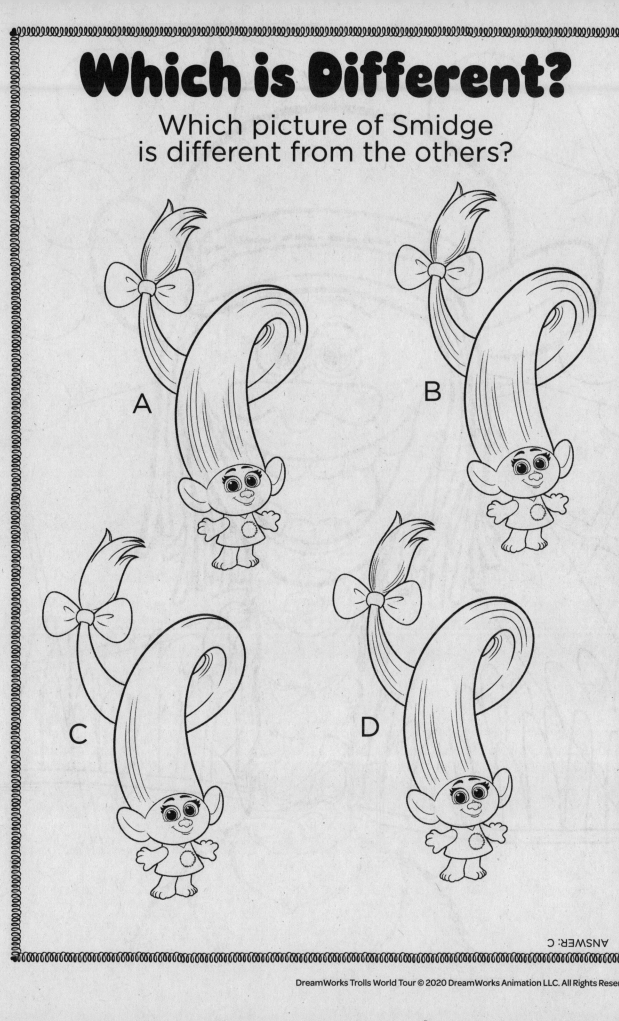

SQUARES

Taking turns, connect a line from one flower to another. Whoever makes the line that completes the square puts his or her initial in the square. The person with the most squares at the end of the game wins!

A-MAZE-ING JOURNEY

Help Prince D get to Vibe City!

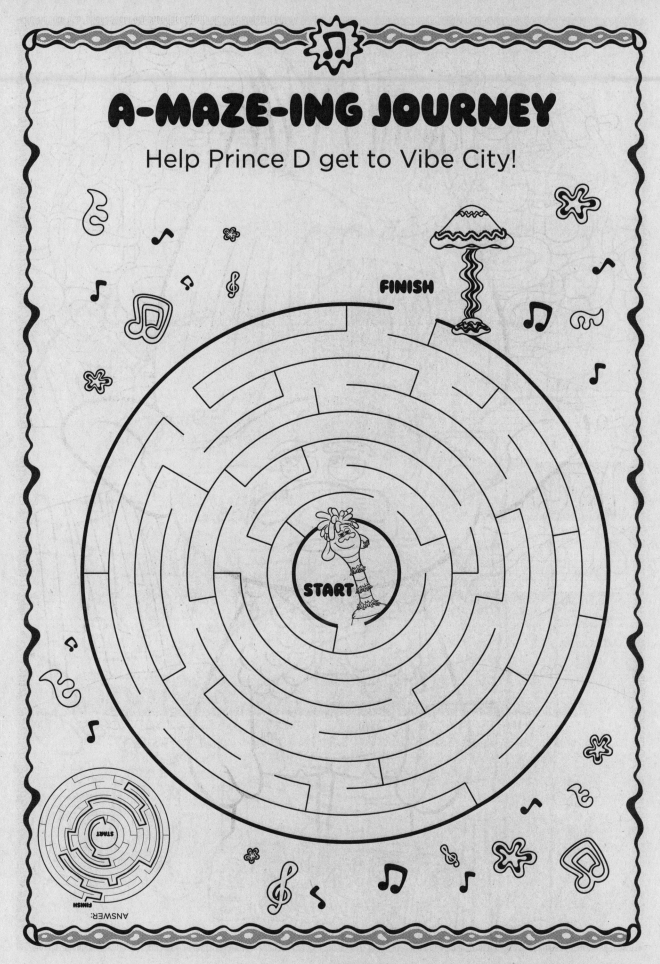

FINISH

START

ANSWER:

START

FINISH

TIC-TAC-TOE

Play a game of Tic-Tac-Toe with a friend!

Interlock

Complete the puzzle by using the words from the list.

LOVE · PARTY
VIBES · TOGETHER
WORLD · TOUR

ROW 02   SECTION T   ADMIT ONE

ANSWER:
PARTY
TOGETHER
VIBES
D
LOVE
TOUR
WORLD
S

DreamWorks Trolls World Tour © 2020 DreamWorks Animation LLC. All Rights Reserved.

Can you find 5
HEARTS
hidden in the picture?

DRAW

The Techno Trolls are mermaids and
live underwater in Techno Reef.
Draw a picture of yourself
as a Techno Troll!

Find Fourteen

Look forward, backward, up, down, and diagonally to find the word below 14 times.

 **SING**

```
S I N I N S G N S I
I S I N G G N I S G
N I S G I N S S I N
G N I S S I N I N N
N G I I V S I N G I
I N G N S I I G I S
G I S G I N G N I S
G I S I N G N G G I
S N I G N S S I I G
```

ANSWER:

UNSCRAMBLE

Unscramble the words listed below.

________________ INKG

________________ OLXRLTE

________________ EOCNTH

________________ EREF

________________________ ATEARTHBE

________________________ MMIDERAS

________________________ ILSHTG

ANSWER: KING TROLLEX, TECHNO REEF, HEARTBEAT, MERMAIDS, LIGHTS

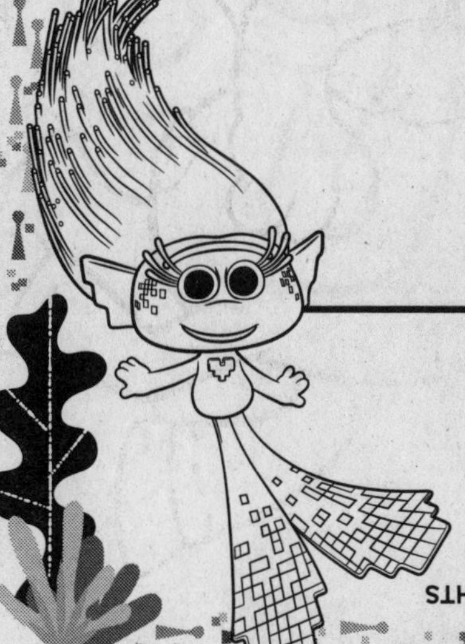

LET'S DRAW!

Trace the gray lines to finish
the drawing of King Trollex!

Shadow Match

Which shadow matches the Troll kid?

Use the grid to draw HICKORY.

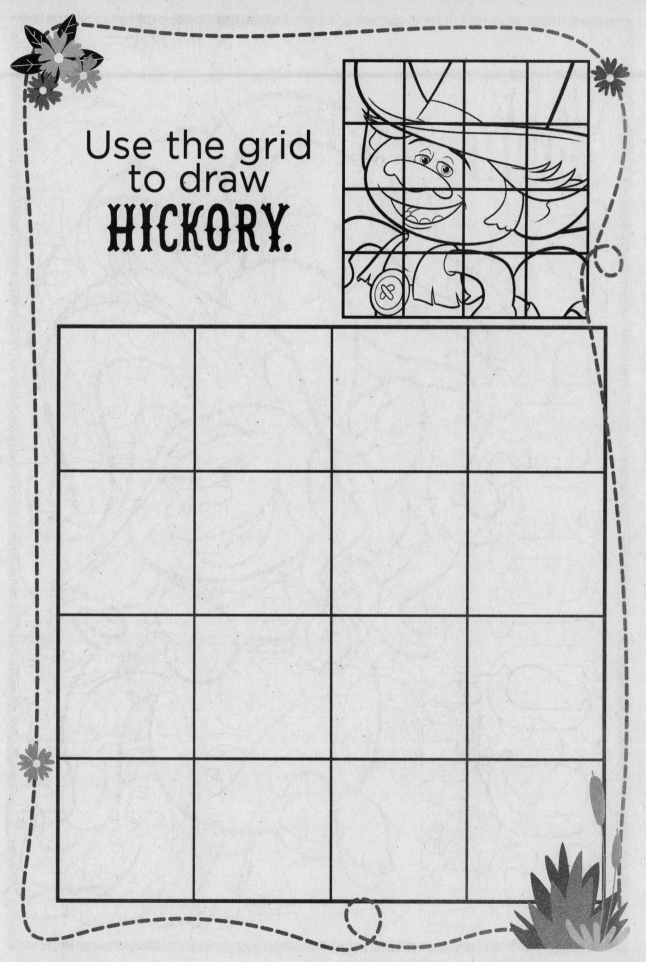

TRANSFER

Using the paths, transfer the letters into the circles below to unscramble the word.

N H T O E C

How many words can you make from the letters in the phrase below?

Dance Your Amp Off

--- --- --- --- --- ---   --- --- --- --- --- ---

--- --- --- --- --- ---   --- --- --- --- --- ---

--- --- --- --- --- ---   --- --- --- --- --- ---

--- --- --- --- --- ---   --- --- --- --- --- ---

--- --- --- --- --- ---   --- --- --- --- --- ---

--- --- --- --- --- ---   --- --- --- --- --- ---

--- --- --- --- --- ---   --- --- --- --- --- ---

Dot-to-Dot

Go dot-to-dot to finish the picture of Queen Barb!

Which Path?

Which path leads
Cloud Guy to
Satin and Chenille?

A   B   C

Your
Answer

MISSING PIECE

Find the missing piece of the image and finish the drawing of Queen Essence!

Secret Message

Use the key to decipher
the secret message.

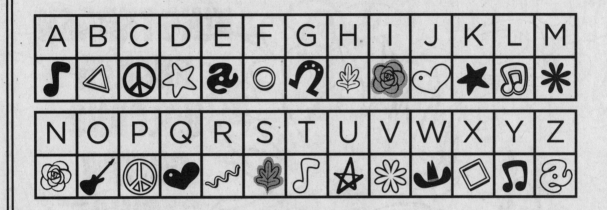

DreamWorks Trolls World Tour © 2020 DreamWorks Animation LLC. All Rights Reserved.

Word Search

Search the next page for
the words listed below.

KING THRASH
ROCKER
VOLCANO
GUITAR
STRINGS
BARB
DEBBIE
RIFF

ANSWER:

```
U D E B B I E P B S
B U S J E B H R E G
R O C K E R A F N K
A S E L A T B F N I
B I Z D L X I F I R
S F L U L G F R T T
M D G W C N J E G S
A W O L C A N O B A
K I N G T H R A S H
```

```
K I N G T H R A S H
W V O L C A N O B A
M D G W C N J E Q S
S F L U L G F R T T
B I Z D I L X I C R
A S E L A T B F N I
R O C K E R A F K N
B U S J E B H R E G
U D E B B I E P B S
```

Count 'Em Up

How many music notes do you see?

Your
Answer

Troll Match

Which two pictures of Riff are the same?

Follow the Path

Find your way through the
puzzle by following the word
A-M-P-I-T-U-P in order.

START

(A) M P I U F I A Y M
W S L T K C P L I P
H Q J U C H T F K D
U H C P O D M W F P
R P M A B U P A M G
Z I E D K T E G P V
L T O B R I V T I G
O U P A M P A U N J
N I S E J T B (P) A M

FINISH

SQUARES

Taking turns, connect a line from one roller skate to another. Whoever makes the line that completes the square puts his or her initial in the square. The person with the most squares at the end of the game wins!

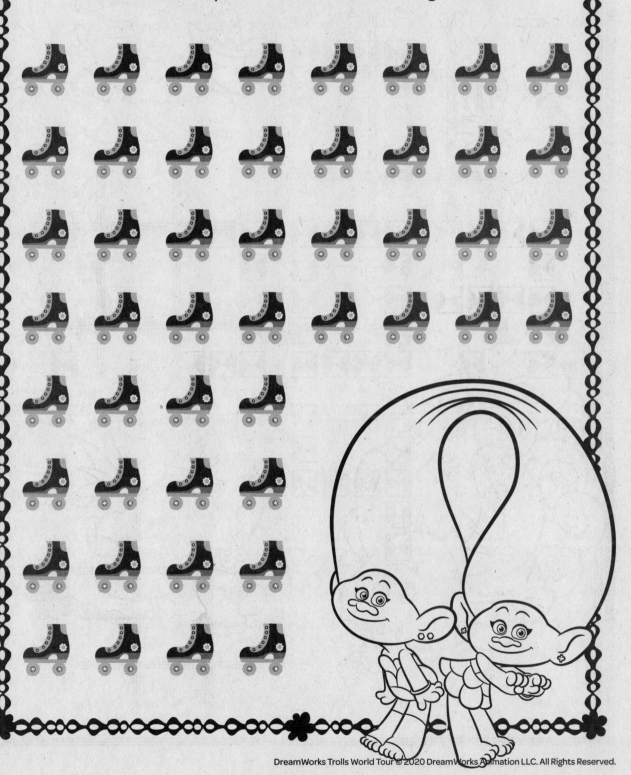

TIC-TAC-TOE

Play a game of Tic-Tac-Toe with a friend!